CAITHNESS AND SUTHERLAND

GHOSTS WITCHES FOLKLORE LEGENDS STRANGE MYSTERIES AND SECRETS

LANG SYNE
PUBLISHING

PUBLISHER'S NOTE

Stories in Part One are reprinted by permission of the copyright holders, from 'The Lure of the Kelpie — Fairy and Folk Tales of the Highlands' by Helen Drever, first published by the Moray Press in 1943. Stories in Part Two are from 'Selected Highland Folk Tales and Legends' and 'More Highland Folk Tales' by R MacDonald Robertson, edited by Jeremy Bruce-Watt and published by Oliver and Boyd. This material is reprinted by permission of their successors, Longmans U.K.
This edition was published by Lang Syne Publishers Ltd, Unit 1C, Whitecrook Centre, 78 Whitecrook Street, Clydebank, G81 1QF and printed at the same address by the Darnley Press. Original illustrations are by John Mackay.

ISBN 185 217 194 4

INTRODUCTION

Who was John de Grot, the man who gave John O' Groats its name? What kind of wicked creatures were the kelpies and why were they more feared than ghosts and witches? How did hundreds of little brown fairies come tumbling out of the forbidden box demanding: 'Give us work! Give us work!' Where did a man steal a mermaid's sealskin coat and force her to be his wife?

These are just some of the questions answered in this fascinating collection of folk tales and legends from Caithness and Sutherland, the two most northerly counties of Britain.

Helen Drever's stories in Part One are written in a fairy tale stlye that will delight children of all ages! And if you like old legends, be they true, corrupted or plain unbelievable, then the stories in Part Two by R MacDonald Robertson will capture your imagination. Both writers travelled extensively throughout the North and many of the stories were taken down orally from folk who heard them at ceilidhs, passed down from generation to generation.

Find out about the descendants of a monster, complete with tails, who were said to be living within 100 miles of Bonar Bridge, the night lights that foretell disaster, the farmer haunted by a two headed dog, the sacred fires that cured diseased cattle, the death secret of a fisherman's gold earring, the phantom minister, the treasure secret of a man trapped in gold chains for eternity unless he is discovered and freed, the loch full of water horses, the terror of a thief who stole a dead sailor's clothes, the girl who died of a broken heart at the Queen Mother's castle, the phantom shepherd who froze in the snow, the giant worm that terrorised an entire district, the grim prediction that five bodies a day would be washed up on the Caithness shore, plus many other strange and amazing secrets from the rugged lands of the North!

PART ONE

The story of John o' Groats

"What went ye out for to see?
A rock in the midst of the wave?
Where the north winds bluster and rave;
Caledonia's outermost rim,
Kissing the ocean grim.
Skerry and holm and stack,
Fringed with the foam and the wrack —
This went ye out for to see?
Not in the midst of the wave,
Rocks where the north winds rave —
But the house of the famous John Groat."

PROFESSOR BLACKIE.

Nearly five hundred years ago the people who lived in the extreme north-east of Caithness got a surprise one day, when a strange, foreign-looking man, who said that he had brought them a letter from the King, arrived at that out-of-the-way corner.

Very few people there could have seen a letter from a real live King, so the document was examined curiously by the whole district.

The letter commended the bearer of it — John de Grot — to His Majesty's subjects in the far north as "an honest man, a good sailor, and a useful fellow to have among them." At one time the people of the far north wouldn't have bothered about what any Scottish King said; but James the Fourth was different, for he had taken the trouble to come several times to the Highlands in order to get to know his subjects there, and had shown them that he wished to be friendly. The great Chiefs had been invited to meet him, and they had been glad to offer him their loyalty.

So the stranger who carried his letter was received by these north country clansfolk as one of themselves, because of the King's letter. Some of them said that John de Grot was Flemish, and some that he was a Dutchman, but whichever he was didn't really matter, for he settled down and lived among them like an ordinary Caithness man.

He found that a ferry to carry people between Caithness and the Orkney Islands was very badly required, so, being a capable boatman, he started a service for that purpose, from the beach that lies between the two rocky headlands — Huna Head and Duncansby Head.

The fare which he charged his passengers is said to have been a groat — which is a coin worth fourpence — and the beach came to be known as John o' Groats — both because of his name and because of the fare.

He married a Caithness woman, and in time eight sons were born to them, and as they grew up they were able to help their father with the ferry boats, of which he now had several, and John de Grot became known as a flourishing man of affairs. Once a year the Grots had a family gathering, at which they feasted royally, to celebrate John's success in life.

The sons gradually took wives from the district, but somehow the annual parties became less happy, for they all became jealous of each other. One wife would say that *her* husband ought to be at the head of the table beside his father; and another would say, "Not at all! Why should he?"

The constant bickering worried poor old John, and one day, after an unusually quarrelsome party, he went and selected a spot on the beach and began making measurements there. "What *can* our father be doing?" the sons said to their mother, but she just shook her head.

As the months went on a strange house arose on the beach. It had eight sides and in the middle of each side there was a door. Old John worked in the house by himself, and neither his sons nor their wives were allowed to see inside it.

The day of the yearly family gathering came round again, and they assembled, as usual, in the cottage in which they had all been born. But the table was bare! Where was the feast? John gave them a humorous smile and said, "Come with me"; and he and his wife and the sons and their wives all walked over to the strange new house on the beach.

"Now," John said, "for years your father and mother have been troubled with your quarrelling about which of you should be at the head of your father's table. Let there now be peace among you, for in this house you will find a table which has eight sides. Each side has a door that opens on itself and each one of you is now the head of his own table!" — And I am glad to say that that settled all the trouble in John o' Groat's family.

John died at a great age, and so in time did his sons. For many years after they were all gone the queer old eight-sided house stood there to show how a wise man settled his family's quarrels; and Caithness people from far and near used to go and look at it. And now, although there is not a stick or stone of the old house left, people who come to Caithness from all over the world still say, "Let us go and see John o' Groats!"

The lure of the Kelpie

SUTHERLAND AND LOCHABER

The people in the Highlands used to fear the Water-horse — or the Kelpie, as it was called — even more than ghosts, fairies and witches and other uncanny beings.

The kelpie was an evil creature that lived in water. He made his home in lochs and rivers and even in waterfalls, and he preyed on human beings. People said that the Devil was his father. He had the power of changing himself into any living form — human or animal — but the disguise which he most often assumed was that of a beautiful horse. That is why he was often called the water-horse.

When he had changed his form he would graze quietly at the roadside, splendidly harnessed and groomed, and sure that in a very short while he would attract attention and caresses from passers-by. And woe betide those who touched his mane or his glossy coat with even a finger, for he possessed a magnetic power that held fast to human touch and he never released his prey.

He would soar into the air like a streak of lightning, carrying with him his helpless victim to the nearest water; and next day nothing would be left but some horrible traces of his crime.

People were very brave about him in the day-time. "What nonsense they'll be talking!" they'd say. "Indeed and indeed there's no such thing as a water-horse at all!" But at night-time it was a very different story, for then the Highlander would look with cold fear at any horse at the roadside that loomed up out of the darkness; and thankful indeed he would be when he was safely past the creature!

A story is told about a kelpie which lived in a loch on the west coast of Sutherland, and which was particularly fond of the flesh of children.

One day he took his usual shape, and when the children came out of school the first thing they noticed was a fine horse quietly grazing at the roadside.

"Look you! Isn't that the lovely horse!" cried one boy.

"Yes, indeed. Come on, and let us mount him!" cried another — and they ran towards the animal, and up they got.

"Come on, room for one more," they cried; and child after child scrambled on the horse's broad back, until there was only one boy left.

"Come you, Dougal," the leader cried. "There's room for one more — or is it a coward you are?" and he laughed scornfully.

"Of that I am not so sure," said Dougal.

For something warned him to keep away, but rather than be jeered at he went towards the horse and just touched its coat with one finger. And then he felt an uncanny power drawing him nearer, and he knew that something was wrong. Quickly whipping his knife out of his pocket he gave a great slash at his finger and released himself, but his finger stuck to the horse's coat!

The kelpie — as indeed it was — gave a great snort and then, to the horror of the teacher, who had just appeared at the door of the school, he soared up into the air in the direction of the loch. He poised himself above it for a second and then with a great splash kelpie and children and all disappeared below its surface. Next morning all the mothers in the glen were childless, except the mother of fingerless Dougal!

But there were occasions when the kelpie was not so successful with his victims.

In Lochaber one of these creatures used to take the form of a man and make himself agreeable to the girls of the countryside.

There was one girl much prettier thah the rest, whom the kelpie had admired for a long time, without ever having the chance of speaking to her. She was the dairymaid in the big farm nearby, and her name was Mhairi.

But his chance came when the farmer built a shieling (or cottage) away up Glen Maillie; for in the glen was the waterfall behind which the kelpie lived. And Mhairi was sent to the shieling to take charge of the cows and their milk. Many girls would not have cared to live in such a lonely place, but Mhairi was a brave-hearted girl and she never thought of danger.

But one night in the gloaming, when she was sitting at her wheel and winding her distaff in the firelight, there came a slow step to her open door, and a voice said, "Can I come in, Mhairi?" Thinking it must be one of the herd lads from the mountains, Mhairi called out, "Of course, whoever you are. Come you in, and sit by the fire." And a man stepped into the room — rather a strange-looking fellow, who did not speak much, but who sat and stared at her from a dark corner.

Night after night he came, and always as he came in he said, in the Gaelic, words that meant something like this:

"Listen you to the kelpie man
That lives deep under the waterfall in Glen Maillie,
And that comes every night with the gloaming
To sit and gaze upon Mhairi."

He always brought a number of little trout with him, and in the course of the evening he roasted and ate them one after the other, saying as he ate each one, "See you, how I roast my trout, that you may learn it too. Trout by trout — trout by trout!" until Mhairi felt a strange eerie feeling come over her and wondered if he was putting a spell on her. And as he cooked and ate his fish he ogled her with such horrible glances that she got frightened, and at last one day she fled down the glen to tell her mother that she no longer felt safe in the shieling.

The farmer didn't want to lose Mhairi, and he promised her that somehow or other he would get rid of her troublesome visitor, so he went and consulted an old witch-wife. "Listen you, Morag," he said, "how am I to get rid of this kelpie fellow? — for Mhairi is a good dairywoman and I don't want to lose her." And Morag said, "The only thing that the kelpie is afraid of is the feel of boiling water on his feet. Give him a good souse with that and he will run back to his father, the Devil, and never bother Mhairi more."

The farmer, grateful for this hint from the witch-wife, took his way to the shieling, and having arrived there he lit Mhairi's fire and placed on it a great pot of water to heat. Then he dressed himself in clothes and a cap of Mhairi's which he found, and he sat down at the wheel to wind the distaff, as Mhairi was accustomed to do.

And as the gloaming fell there came the usual footsteps and the creature came in, saying as usual:

"Listen you to the kelpie man
That lives deep under the waterfall in Glen Maillie,
And that comes every night with the gloaming
To sit and gaze upon Mhairi."

Then he sat down, and began, as usual, to roast his trout. But the figure sitting at the wheel, and winding away so silently, never turned a head, and the kelpie began to be suspicious. He threw some sticks on the fire, and when they blazed up he saw that he had been tricked, and he started up, saying angrily:

"You may be turning the distaff cleverly enough,
But now I see the eyes of you
And now I see the nose of you
And now I see the whiskers of you,
And it's not Mhairi you are, at all! — "

and he sprang angrily at his deceiver.

But the farmer was quicker. With one spring he reached the pot on the fire and swung its boiling contents over the kelpie's feet, which immediately showed as cloven hoofs where before they had been human feet!

The kelpie screamed out with rage and pain, "What's your name?" and the farmer answered in the Gaelic, "'Tis me! 'Tis me!" Several of the kelpie's brothers hearing the noise came to meet him, asking, "Who has done this to you, brother?" and the kelpie said, as the farmer had, "'Tis me! 'Tis me!" Upon which the other kelpies said, "Then if 'twas yourself that hurt yourself, let yourself help yourself," and they returned in disgust to the waterfall, leaving the scalded kelpie to make his own way back.

And Mhairi came back to the shieling in the mountains, and never more at the gloaming did she hear the words:

"Listen you to the kelpie man
That lives deep under the waterfall in Glen Maillie,
And that comes every night with the gloaming
To sit and gaze upon Mhairi."

Mary the Mermaid

A Sutherland folk tale

A summer dawn was breaking on the north-west coast of Sutherland. The sea was at the ebb and Nature was still and beautiful. Even the young crofter, Dougal McVeagh, who had lived all his life in the cottage over the hill, and who knew every stone on the beach, felt that wonderful radiance when the sun rose behind the hill and touched the western sea with loving fingers of light.

"Surely," he thought, "something unusual is moving out therein the little bay — something white and lovely — something that flashes like gold — what can it be?"

Then a ray from the rising sun lit up the figure of a mermaid, who sat out there on a rock combing her lovely golden hair. As Dougal drew nearer to her he noticed a bundle lying on one of the rocks. He picked it up and found it was the skin of a seal, which he carefully refolded and held behind him.

The mermaid saw the movement and started, then, jumping off the rock on which she was sitting, she approached the place where she had left her skin. Seeing that it was gone she began to weep softly and, holding out her hands to Dougal she said:

"Oh, mortal! Why steal from me that which can do little good to you, and which leaves me very poor indeed? Oh, give me back my skin!"

"No, no," said Dougal. "Heaven forbid that Dougal McVeagh should hurt a hair of your lovely head! But I'll not give you back that ugly thing. I'll do far better, for I'll run to my cottage for some lovely clothes that my mother wore when she was young."

"But, mortal," said the mermaid, "I cannot stay. And you must not tempt me, for indeed I must return to the coral caves where I live with my sisters, and where a brave knight of the sea fights the sea-lions and kills the great sea-serpents in my defence. Only last night, in the silver moonlight, he left me to go hunting. What if he has returned to find me gone! Oh, kind mortal, give me my skin and let me go!"

"Lady," said Dougal, "it is by refusing that same skin that I can prove my kindness. Wait you here for me, and I will bring clothes to you in which you will look far prettier, and feel far happier, than you did in that ugly wet skin."

And running to his cottage he was back in a few minutes with the clothes, which, in truth, were very pretty. He laid them on a flat piece of wood which he sent sailing across the water to the mermaid.

When she saw them she laughed with pleasure, and drew the little raft into a cave close by. In a few moments she put them on and came out of the cave, looking — as Dougal was not slow to tell her — the prettiest human maiden ever seen.

"Now come with me to my home," said the delighted Dougal. "My mother used to wish for a daughter called Mary, so

I will call you by the name she loved, and you will stay with me and be my wife."

"Wait just a moment," said the newly christened Mary, as she knelt on a rock above a quiet pool, and looked down admiringly at her reflection in the water. And as she raised herself she said in childish delight:

"Indeed, Dougal, you are quite right. I do look very pretty! Your mother's dress suits me far better than my seal skin, and I will go with you to your cottage."

So Mary the Mermaid went home with Dougal, and he took care to hide the seal skin in a dark corner of the barn.

Time went on and five beautiful children came to Dougal and Mary; and Dougal — when he thought about it at all — felt that that summer dawn long ago had been a lucky one for him.

Mary seemed quite contented, but Dougal never noticed that when a high tide washed up big drifts of seaweed upon the beach she got restless and moody, and went away by herself. And when she was cutting the brackens, which they used for bedding the cattle, she would sigh to herself, and sing softly:

"I am tired, all alone
Cutting brackens, cutting brackens,
I am tired, all alone
Cutting brackens always.
Round the hillocks, o'er the hillocks,
On the hillocks only,
Round the hillocks, on the hillocks,
Oh, this day! So lonely!"

One harvest day when the eldest children were quite big, Dougal with the help of the family was building stooks in the field. So Mary was alone in the cottage when the youngest child came running in with a queer old skin which he had found in the barn. Mary trembled and flushed as she took it from him and hid it away. That night no sleep came to her eyelids, for in her ears the sound of the waves and the voices of her sister mermaids kept echoing from the coral caves below the sea.

At last she stole out of bed, leaving Dougal sound asleep. She stole into the open air, and, as she left the cottage, she threw out her arms as if to call down a blessing on those she was leaving. Then, lifting the seal skin, she raced over the hill to the shore, where she drew on the old skin.

And dawn, which had seen her arrival, now saw her departure; and the rising sun pointed a finger of light at the spot where the waves now closed over "Mary the Mermaid" for ever!

Dougal used to go down to the shore and call "Mary! Mary! Come back to me!" But only the sea-birds and the waves replied to his call. But he knew that Mary had not forgotten, because, every morning, six fine fish were lying on the shore for the cottage breakfast!

Long after Dougal and his children's children were dead, those who came after them were known in the West of Sutherland by the name *"Sliochd na Maighdean Chuain"* — "The Children of the Mermaid."

The Fairies of the Gizzen Brigs

Near Tongue there lived, once upon a time, one of the Mackay Chieftains. He was the lord of all the Reay Country, which was beautiful then as it is now — with its blue lochs, its lofty bens, and its purple moors. Its northern boundary is the seashore, with white sands and a rugged coastline, and here and there a fine sheltered bay.

One of these bays, called the Kyle of Tongue, runs very far inland, and is like a deep, narrow wedge cut out of the land.

Now this wedge used to aggravate the Laird of Reay, because whenever he wanted to call on his sweetheart, who lived directly across the Kyle, he had to go all the way up one side and all the way down the other.

He couldn't cross by boat, because the rocks below were so steep that there was no landing place for a boat on either side.

"If I could only get a bridge built!" he said — and he called all the fairies in the Reay Country into council, hoping they might help him.

"*We* are not bridge-building fairies!" they said. "But perhaps the Witch of Reay can tell you who will help you."

So to the Witch of Reay he went.

"No, Laird of Reay," she said to him. "*I* cannot help you, but I can tell you who can. Send you a messenger to Skian Beg, the Wise Woman of Tarbat, in Ross-shire. She has *working* fairies, whom she can command at will."

So the Laird immediatel;y sent Angus Mackay, one of his clansmen, off to Ross-shire. Angus had a long, long way to walk, but he shortened the distance by going to Dornoch Point and then crossing the Firth by boat to Whiteness Point below Tain.

From there he walked on to Tarbat Ness, where, in a dark hut on the rocky headland, he found the old witch. There she sat, day after day, gazing out to sea; and night after night, talking to the stars.

The Reay man felt very eerie when she turned her strange eyes on him, and said, "Well, Man of Reay, and what brings *you* here to trouble me?"

When he told her what the Reay Witch had said, she answered coldly, "And will you be telling me, Angus Mackay, *why* Skian Beg should help the Laird of Reay at all? Indeed, it is myself never liked him or his."

"But, mother, are you acquaint with the Laird?" asked the astonished man.

"That I am — and with his forbears as far back as 'Angus the Absolute' — who was a proud man and a leader of men; but he was hard — hard!"

Then, with her voice softening, she said, "Ah, but his *lady* was kind. *She* never turned a haughty eye on Skian Beg! So for her sake I will give you the help you ask for the Laird of Reay. Now, wait you here for me, and in a box which you must carry back to him I will give you what the Laird needs. When he gets that he will soon be able to bridge the Kyle of Tongue."

She went away, and soon returned — carrying a large box, which was covered with heather and tied round and round with long grasses. As she handed it to Angus she said:

"Now Man of Reay, carry this back to the Laird, and *remember this!* If you try to look inside this box you will rue the day you were born." Angus thanked her, and walked off with the box under his arm. It was not heavy, but he felt there was something *queer* about it! Indeed, at times he felt sure there was something moving inside it, and he wished very much to know what it could be. As he got farther away from Skian Beg the fear which she had put upon him grew less intense; and by the time he reached his boat at Whiteness Point he felt quite daring.

"Why need I be minding yon old witch?" he said to himself. "For sure there *is* something moving in this box, and I'll just take a peep."

So he broke the grass fastening very cautiously, made a hole in the heather, and then with his dirk he poked a hole in the box.

Well! Angus Mackay got the fright of his life, for from the box sprang hundreds of little brown fairies!

They clambered all over poor Angus, they poked at his eyes and his ears, and they pulled his hair — screaming all the time, "Give us work master! Give us work, give us work! We are working fairies!"

"Oh pity me!" said inquisitive Angus to himself. "What am I to do now, at all?"

He gave a desperate look towards the land. There above the beach was Tain, and beyond that again he saw Tain Hill, so he said, "Go you and strip all the heather off Tain Hill. Quick now! Be going!"

There was a whirr of brown wings, and in a moment they

were gone.

"Isn't that the mercy!" said Angus Mackay to himself. "Now I will be going! And I will take the box and tie it up again and carry it to the Laird. He will never be any the wiser."

He did this, and then hurried to the boat, which was lying high and dry on Whiteness Sands — for the tide had gone back while Angus was away. He pushed it out as quickly as he could, and he had just managed to reach the water when suddenly the air was darkened with the returning fairies.

"Och, och!" said Angus to himself, "and what will I be doing now?"

Again they clambered up on him, screaming, "Give us work, master! Give us work!"

"And is it work you are asking?" he said to them angrily, "when I told you to strip Tain Hill. Indeed! and you hardly away when you were back!"

"Tain Hill is bare, master," they cried. "Look up. There is not even a blade of heather on it."

And sure enough, when he looked, the hill which had been glowing purple was now brown earth! Again they screamed at him, "Give us work, master! Give us work!"

Angus now looked at the water of the Firth, and — "See you," he said, "you must build a bridge that will stretch from here across to Dornoch Point. Make bricks of sand and then spin the sand into ropes with which to bind the bricks together — and go on building until you can walk right across the Firth without wetting your feet. Now be off with you!"

Again the brown wings whirred, and the moment the fairies had gone Angus made for his boat, and — the tide being favourable — he soon reached Dornoch Point, and left the fairies behind.

The fairies got on finely with their work until the tide came up, and then — alas! — the incoming water destroyed all their bricks and the ropes of sand that they had spun.

"Oh dear! Oh dear!" the poor things cried. "All our work is wasted!" So they just had to begin all over again; but they felt that it was very unfair, and some of them cried bitterly in their disappointment. Every day and every night the same thing happened, for you know the tide ebbs and flows twice a day; and all the time the poor fairies struggled away to build the bridge. That happened hundreds of years ago, and do you know, they are working there still! From the point below Tain a line of breakers — which Tain people call "The Gizzen Brigs" — stretches across to Dornoch. They mark the line where the fairies are working. When the tide is low and the water is calm there is only a ripple along the line, and you know that the fairies are laughing and singing among themselves because they think that they are going to finish their bridge some day. But when stormy weather comes the Tain people hear a moaning sound and they say, "Listen to the Gizzen Brigs. How loud they are tonight!" They don't know — although you and I do — that it isn't the Gizzen Brigs at all. It is the sound of the fairies crying because their work is never done!

The first Earl of Ross

In the early summer of 1272, great processions of clansmen daily passed southward from the Northern Highlands. Their movements greatly puzzled the simple folk who lived on the hillsides and in the straths of Sutherland and Ross.

For although these passing companies consisted entirely of picked men, their appearance did not in the least suggest clan raids. Indeed they seemed to be garbed rather for feasting than for war — so fresh were their tartans and tunics, so bright and shining their claymores, dirks and brooches.

Still, the canny Ross-shire folk, curious though they were, took no chances, but viewed the passers-by from safe spots of vantage like the Shoulder of Struie, the high banks of the Red Burn, or the woods of Balnagown. Though even when some of the bairns gave away their retired position by excited screeches, the passing warriors acknowledged their presence only by good-natured waves — it was very puzzling!

Some of the neighbouring clans were speedily recognized.

"That's the Sutherlands! See the Chief — yon big fellow with the black-cock's feather in his bonnet!" an old wife exclaimed.

"Indeed and I'm thinking it's right you are," said another, "but who can *they* be in the green tartan? Is it the Mackays, think you?"

"No, not Mackays, lassie, for the Mackays went by yesterday — do you not mind? But I'm thinking that is the Gunns, from Caithness; for myself saw that same tartan at Ubster when I went with himself to see his sister there, long since."

"Well then, if it is the Gunns that is in it, the Keiths will not be far behind, no, nor the Sinclairs neither."

"But Granny, will we not be seeing Big Ferchard and the Rosses?" said a wee laddie with a tousled red head.

"That will you," said the old body — "if you will be patient. The son of Gille Andreas was never backward — in love or war!"

The pageantry went on, the onlookers still keeping their

distance — until the sight of Farquhar Ross, attended by a goodly company of red-kilted lads, brought them pelting down to the roadside; and so close did they press to the chief that he waved his arms in laughing expostulation.

"Have a care, my darling ones!" he cried, as they pressed round him, some of the boys even fingering his claymore and his dirk.

"Have a care! Myself is only after polishing the weapons — and it a woman's job! See, would it not be a sad thing if one of my own should dull that brightness, and us not right on our way to London Town?"

"To London Town?" said the astounded people. "Then it is war after all?"

"*War?*" laughed Farquhar. "No, not war! It is a ploy, my dears. For we are off at the bidding of Alexander, our good King, to attend him at the crowning of Edward, the new King of England. And indeed ourselves will be showing the Sassenachs the kind of men we can breed in the Highlands!"

"But," said an old fellow, "it is surely new for the King of England to be that far in with the King of Scots?"

"What else would you expect?" said Farquhar, "when his own sister Margaret is wife to the King of Scots? But back with you now, children of my heart, for indeed we must be for off!"

And away went he and his gallant company on the southward trek — like all the rest.

They fell in with hundreds of other Scots, all taking the same road; for every great family or clan had been invited to send its representatives to honour the occasion, and show the flower of Scotland's manhood at the English Court. London was a long way from the Northern Counties, but the Highlanders were hardy fellows, and their march was only a bit longer than usual. And if they felt out of their depth on arriving at the great Capital, they masked their feelings well.

Indeed, the haughty, indifferent way in which they moved among the Sassenachs made a great impression, and their splendid physique and unusual garb attracted nearly as much comment as Royalty itself.

Feasting and pageantry were the order of every day. Each morning saw fresh trials of skill and strength — tournaments and jousting, fencing, wrestling, swordsmanship, and horsemanship. Wrestling was indeed a very special feature of the festivities, for there was at that time at the English Court a French wrestler of great fame, of whom it was written:

"He had sic marveillous strength and had sic craft in wrasling he caist all men yat assailyait him. Notheless he was finallie wanquishit."

One by one the English wrestlers had tried conclusions with him, and each one in turn had been thrown.

Now the English King said to King Alexander:

"Pray you, my brother of Scotland, have you among your people now in London anyone wishful to fight this mighty Norman? Though indeed, after seeing how the greatest wrestlers of our country have failed to vanquish him you might deem it but a waste of time to challenge him."

And the Scots Queen, Margaret, anxious to please her brother and their host, said laughing:

"Nay, brother, is it likely that our Scots countrymen could possibly succeed where the best English wrestlers have failed?"

But King Alexander said:

"Let *me* speak, wife! My brother of England, wrestling is an art much practised in my country; indeed I have among my followers in London several noted wrestlers. They may not, it is true, have the art of this Norman, who has overthrown so many of your countrymen; yet will I find one capable of trying a round or two with him. After all, it will be no disgrace to a Scottish wrestler should he fall in such distinguished company!"

And the English King — privately considering the trial but wasted time — graciously agreed to a meeting.

The Scots went very carefully about the selection of a challenger. All the heads of the clans were called into council, and a leet of the best Scots wrestlers was drawn up. Name after name was eliminated from the list, until only one was left — the name of Farquhar Ross; who now challenged the great French wrestler to a trial of skill.

On the day appointed there was a full attendance of the English Court, for noble Lords and Ladies were eager to see this meeting between the French wrestler and the venturesome Scot. They fully expected the result to be short, sharp, and decisive — for the former.

But when the two men stepped into the ring it had to be allowed that the Scot, in physique at any rate, fully matched his opponent.

The Norman, arrogant and swaggering, bowed with foreign grace to the spectators, the while the Scot stood, quiet and watchful, eyeing his opponent carefully.

The first rounds were uneventful, but the Ross men said;

"Watch you Ferchard! He is but taking the measure of his man."

While the Englishmen said:

"Wait until the Norman attacks!"

But what was their amazement to see the *Scot* attacking, and the Frenchman defending!

Fast and furious waged the fight, and back — back went the Frenchman, striving vainly for position and opportunity, against the calculating mercilessness of a foe who was mightier and more skilful than himself!

And almost in shorter time than it takes to tell, the Norman was down — and out!

What a scene of excitement! Lovely ladies rushed into the arena and threw their arms about the new champion, who laughingly protested!

"Indeed and indeed, my misguided fair ones, and isn't it the good thing that my own lady in far off Ross cannot see her Ferchard at this same moment! See now, jewels, untwine your arms, for indeed I have not the time to spend in fighting all the nobles that would need to challenge me this day on your account!"

And he was sincerely relieved when his too fervid admirers had to give way that he might receive the congratulations of Royalty. If those offered by the English King left, perhaps, something to be desired — for had not this Scotsman prevailed where English wrestlers had failed? — there was no lack of warmth on the part of King Alexander. And as the new champion bent his knee to his master, the King said:

"Farquhar Ross, for your notabill wassilage of this day we doe confer on you the Erldome of Ross!" — and the men of Ross gave a shout that shook the rafters.

Farquhar gave the credit of his victory to a vow made before the fight, that, if he should conquer the Norman he — being a Priest's son — would found an Abbey of the first religious Order whose members he should meet on his way back to Ross-shire.

On his way to the North he fell in with two white canons — or monks — of Whithorn Abbey, in Galloway, and he took them home to Ross-shire, where, at Fearn, by Kincardine, he founded his Abbey. Some 140 yeas ago, it is said, one wall of the building still stood.

But long before that time another Abbey had been built at New Fearn in Easter Ross, a memorial of days long gone — and of the prowess of Farquhar, the first Earl of Ross.

PART TWO

Introduction to Mermaids

From time to time come reports of queer creatures seen around the Scottish coasts. Merfolk were, of course, the traditional inhabitants of the briny deep, and Highland and island lore teems with allusions to the mermaids who dwell "Fathoms deep beneath the wave, stringing beads of glistening pearl." Often they come up from the sea-caves to disport themselves on the shore, and are to be seen in the quiet bays, floating on the surface of the water and mingling their voices with the breeze. Those possessed with vivid imagination might even see the kraken and the sea-serpent and other wonderful animals, and where the merman and the mermaid are concerned, there are histories of the appearance of these monsters. There are many people who assert that they have seen the mermaid.

While I disbelieve the authenticity of these stories, I do not mean to deny the existence of large marine animals having analogies to the serpent; the conger eel we know is such an animal; I have seen one over nine feet long, and there may be even longer ones — but such animals do not come to the surface. The only sea snake that has been examined by naturalists in our waters turned out to be a putrid species of shark — the *squalus maximus.* Yet all the newspapers gave accounts of this as a real animal, and endowed it with feet, which do not belong to serpents. Sea snakes seen by American and Norwegian captains have generally been a company of porpoises, the rising and sinking of which in lines would give somewhat the appearance of the coils of a snake. The kraken, or island-fish, is still more imaginary. Immense numbers of enormous *urticae marinae,* or blubbers, have been seen in the north seas, and in some of the Norwegian fiords, and often these beautiful creatures give colour to the water; but it is exceedingly improbable that an animal of this genus should ever be as big — even as a whale. As for hands and a finny tail, these are entirely contrary to the analogy of nature and I disbelieve the mermaid upon philosophical principles. The dugong and manatee are the only animals combining the functions of the mammalia with some of the characters of fishes, that can be imagined even as a link in this part of the order of nature. Many of these stories have been founded upon the long-haired seal seen at a distance; others on the appearance of the common seal under peculiar circumstances of light and shade.

Some people do not understand upon what philosophical principles one should deny the existence of the mermaid. They are not necessarily acquainted with all the animals that inhabit the bottom of the sea; and they cannot help thinking there must have been some foundation for the fable of the Tritons and Nereids, to say nothing of the ocean divinities, Neptune and Aphrodite. Such an animal, if created, could not long exist; and, with scarcely any locomotive powers, would be the prey of other fishes, formed in a manner more suited to their element. I have seen a most absurd fabrication of a mermaid, exposed as a show-piece in London, and another, some years ago, in an Edinburgh carnival, said to have been found in the Chinese seas, and bought for a fabulous sum of money. The head and bust of two different apes were ingeniously fastened to the lower part of a dippered salmon, which had the fleshy fin, and all the distinct characters of the *salmo salar:* and yet, there were people who believed this to be a real animal.

Most zoologists discount the mermaid theory. They believe that the creature which inspired seamen's stories of beautiful fish-tailed women is a manatee, a vegetarian mammal from tropic seas; but it is far from beautiful: nor has it long hair to comb, and, saddest of all, it has a bristly moustache. Like Jonah's Whale, or the Loch Ness Monster, one might surmise that the mermaid is what is alleged to have been described in a homily given by an Edinburgh divinity student many years ago at Professor Davidson's class as — "just a big cod!"

However, as the following stories demonstrate, not evryone agrees!

Caithness Mermaids

A slender white hand rose above the water

Many mermaids have been reported and vouched for in the far north-east of Scotland.

A Miss Mackay wrote an account of her own experience in 1809 while walking with a friend along the desolate coast of Caithness. She saw what looked like a human face above the water, but decided that it could not belong to a human being, as the sea was too wild and wintry for anyone to be bathing; and besides, the object disappeared for long periods at a time under the water. Miss Mackay could not on the other hand agree with her practical-minded friend's suggestion that they were looking on the body of some drowned animal, tossed to and fro by the waves; for every now and then a slender white hand rose above the water and tossed back a long mane of green hair!

The lady was convinced that she had seen a mermaid; and when her report was published, James Munro, schoolmaster at Reay, wrote a letter to a London newspaper describing how, twenty years before, he had seen what he took to be a mermaid in Sandside Bay. He has been walking *"an gob na tuinne"* (at the water's edge) when he saw sitting on a rock jutting out into the sea a female figure "in the action of combing its hair, which flowed about its shoulders, and was of a light brown colour."

"It remained on the rock," Mr Munro wrote, "three or four minutes after I had observed it, and then dropped into the sea, from whence it did not reappear to me. I had a distant view of the features." He concluded his letter with the words:—

"I can only say of a truth that it was only by seeing the phenomenon that I was perfectly convinced of its existence."

Prisoner for eternity in cave of treasures

A Caithness fisherman, walking on the shore one morning, saw a beautiful girl sitting on a rock, singing as she combed the long yellow hair that fell over her lovely shoulders. He saw that she had a tail like a fish, and knew that the was looking on a "*maighdean mhara*" (mermaid). Approaching quietly, he clasped her round the waist. She looked up at him; and in that moment came the realisation that each was meant for the other.

From that time the young man kept daily tryst with the

The maid of the sea brought jewels

maid of the sea who brought him gorgeous jewels, gold, and silver, which she said she found among the wrecks of ships in the Pentland Firth. Neighbours began to wonder about the source of his sudden wealth which, alas, soon went to his head. He demanded more and more treasures, which he gave in presents to the girls of the district; and while dallying with them often forgot to keep his tryst with the mermaid, who grew jealous, and upbraided him for his unfaithfulness.

One day she was waiting for him in a boat, in which she offered to take him to a cavern near Duncansby Head, where she kept guard over all the treasure ever lost in the Firth. Overjoyed by the prospect of such wealth, he jumped into the boat, and they sailed away to the wonderful cave.

When they reached it, he fell asleep to the sound of her singing; and when he awoke he found himself secured by golden chains in the innermost recesses of the cave, surrounded by lumps of gold and bars of siver.

> "Bags of fiery opals, sapphires, amethysts,
> Jacinths, harxtopaz, grass-green amethysts,
> Beauteous rubies, sparkling diamonds."
>
> MARLOWE.

There, according to the legend, he has been confined ever since; and whoever finds the cave (and overcomes the mermaid) will have jewels worth a king's ransom.

Merfolk

Bodach Capan Dhearg

The "merfolk" were the traditional inhabitants of the sea. There are few accounts of mermen; but Highland and Island lore teems with allusions to the mermaids who dwelt —

> "Fathoms deep beneath the wave,
> Stringing beads of glistening pearl"

and who often came up from the sea-caves to disport themselves on the shore, and were to be seen in the quiet bays, floating on the surface of the water and mingling their voices with the sighing breeze.

To this day, belief in merfolk, the traditional inhabitants of the briny deep, is rife, especially in the north-west coastal districts of Sutherland.

Mermen fight savagely if entangled in fish-nets

Mermen are known by their red caps which they wear (hence the term — *"Bodach Capan Dhearg"*) when they disport themselves amid the breakers, while mermaids on the other hand are said, on occasion, to come up from the sea-caves to recline on the shore in quiet bays and are recognised by their reddish-yellow curly hair with wreaths of sea-weed round their necks and shoulders. They are believed to mingle their voices with the sighing breeze, but these mermen are said to fight savagely if entangled in fish-nets, and unless instantly released cast death-spells upon the neighbourhood.

During August, 1949, mermen were sighted off Craig More in the Parish of Kinlochbervie by several crofters and sailors on more than one occasion.

In the superstitious belief of the North, seals held a far higher place than any other of the lower animals. They were believed to have a mysterious connection with the human race, and to have the power of assuming human form and faculties.

Seals occasionally lift themselves perpendicularly out of the water, exposing half their bodies, and look as like the representation of a mermaid as possible. The wild and mournful cry of the seal is difficult to describe — something between the mew of a cat and the howl of a dog in distress — a weird and unpleasant sound which harmonises with the wild scenery of their surroundings. Highlanders are by no means prepossessed in favour of the good looks of a seal or *"sealgh"* as they term it. "You are a *sealgh,*" is an expression of disgust which, when uttered by one crofter to another, is considered a great insult and a climax to every known term of reproach.

In Caithness, seals were said to be "fallen angels"; and a popular saying in the North is that they are *"clann righ fo gheasaibh"* (king's children under enchantments). Their origin is explained as follows:—

The widowed King of Lochlinn married for a second time a lady skilled in the Black Art, who by its means strove to get rid of her step-children. It took her seven years and seven days to perfect a plan; and at the end of that time she put the royal children under a powerful *"geas"* (spell) by which they were transformed into seals — neither fish nor flesh. When at sea they would yearn for the land and when on land would long for the sea "as long as the waves beat upon the shore." They were allowed to resume their original human form three times a year at full moon.

It was considered for a long time to be most unlucky and nothing short of murder, to kill a seal, and many tales are told of the fate that befell any brave enough to perform the dire deed. Misfortune was said to dog the footsteps of such a man till the day he died — like the punishment of Coleridge's Ancient Mariner who shot the sacred albatross.

A Sea Bride for Hector

A story told by W J Mackay, F.S A. Scot, Skerray, Sutherland.

In the middle of the eighteenth century there lived on the banks of a river in the Mackay country a man known as "Big Hector." His great delight was to wander along the shores of the bay near his homestead, where this stream flowed into the sea. Among the flotsam amd jetsam cast on the beach he could be found, and especially during dark winter nights when the wind would be howling through the high cliffs, which sent a pang of fear through the hearts of the bravest inhabitants. The stronger the elements of Nature, the greater did the desire appeal to Hector to wade among the surf in the hours of darkness. Such was his love for this kind of life that he was shunned by many and left alone to his desires; but this did not seem to affect him. He attended to his solitary cow, cooked his own meals and did not interfere with anybody. When he did speak, his talk was always of the sea, and the strange creatures which dwelt there; but few believed his tales.

In this mode of life he continued to live for well over thirty years, until one morning, following one of the greatest storms known within living memory, he surprised his neighbours by his extraordinary activity around his croft. He seemed much happier and more industrious than usual and it was observed that he seemed to have left off his former habits. He, however, evaded any enquiry into his affairs, and it was no small wonder when within a year of this strange change in his manner, the cries of a young child were heard from the open door of his cottage. Despite such happenings, the inside of his house was outwith the gaze of his neighbours. He would not encourage them in any way, nor would he satisfy their curiosity in regard to the cries they heard issuing from within. So it was no small wonder when it was whispered from mouth to mouth that Hector had been taken command of by the "Wee Folk." His way of life just desired that and what could be expected — what more could he expect? The ways of a child, however, are the same in all ages and in all places, the wonder of what lies outside their home sets them exploring. A passing neighbour, herding his cow along the banks of the river, happened to lift up his head and on seeing the child, he, like one possessed, left everything and ran towards the village, shouting as he went that Hector had a child.

As years rolled on, Hector seldom went along the shores of the bay. The villagers occasionally visited him and became friendly with his mermaid wife and child, Peter. Peter joined in the life and laughter of the other children of the community, as he was now about five years old. It was, however, noticeable that Hector would not allow anyone near the thatch of his cottage.

One morning, Hector and his young son went for fuel to the moor. As they rounded the turn of the hill, the mermaid mother came to the door of her home, and her sobs and yearning cries after her son were heard by most of the villagers.

An hour or two later, Hector was on his return journey with his son running by his side, when suddenly, letting out a piercing cry, he threw down his creel of peats, and hastened towards his croft.

A wall of foam could be clearly seen moving towards the open sea, and the music of the seals floated over the water.

Hector went straight to the thatched roof of his house, took one look, and then rushed inside his cottage. No one was there, and his hidden treasure was gone. The veil of his wife had disappeared. As long as he could hide this from her, she was his; but now she had managed to get possession of it, and had gone back to her ocean castle.

Hector dashed along the banks of the river; but the procession heading seaward increased their speed, and all he could hear was the music and splashing of the waters.

Broken-hearted and dismayed he returned to his lonely croft. His son tried to console him, but could not do so.

The following morning, he again went to the river's brink, and there he found a large salmon on its bank. This followed morning after morning. One night he kept watch, and sure enough the old seal came up the river with a salmon in its mouth which it laid on the water's edge.

Peter grew up to be a fine young man and married. No one knew so much about the sea and its ways as he did, likewise the generations which followed him.

Why my collie howled in terror

The following story was told to me in Gaelic by the late Alexander Gunn, Balchrick (a few miles north of Kinlochbervie), Sutherland, who in June, 1939 was introduced to me by Donald MacLeod, the former laird of the district. The mermaid in question is alleged to have been seen by Mr Gunn off "Rudha an Fhir Leithe," and his statement is corroborated by witnesses who were present at the interview during which I took notes.

Sandwood Bay, the most north-westerly beach on the British mainland, lies about seven miles south of Cape Wrath lighthouse. It is a wild and inaccessible place. On the south bank of Loch Sandwood was the ruined homestead of the last of the Mackays of Sandwood. Here are only the winds and the waves, and the reflections of the brooding hills, piled in the background in aloof majesty. It is a haunted region with a timeless mystery all its own. Sandwood is described by Seton Gordon as "the most beautiful place on all the West Coast of Scotland."

This district is locally called "The Land of Mermaids," and is a perfect setting for supernatural beings. Numberless waves rush constantly shorewards, falling exhausted on a beach of great sand-dunes that stretches for miles. There is nothing for the eye but mingling shades of grey, and nothing for the ear but the rush and roar of the breakers. Sign of life is nowhere visible. Travellers have told of singing sands: those of Sandwood do not sing, but whisper with every rustle of the breeze as they slide over the hulks of the wrecked ships which lie half buried along the shore. All over is a sense of unbelievable solitude and wonderment. Only the gulls scream overhead like the souls of drowned mariners lured to their doom by the maidens of the sea.

"On Old Christmas night — January 5 — 1900," began the story-teller, "I was going round after sheep between Sheigra and Sandwood Loch. While walking along the edge of the rocky head-lands, I noticed that one of my sheep had fallen down a gully about three miles South-west of Sandwood Bay, known as 'Rudha an Fhir Leithe.' As it was low tide, I descended the cliff towards the seashore to take it up. When I reached the bottom, my collie dog suddenly let out an agonised howl as it crouched in terror close to my feet, with hair bristling, ears set back, and tail between its legs. I looked up. What I saw was sudden and unexpected. It took my breath away.

"To my astonishment, I observed right above me what I at first took to be a human being reclining on a ledge of rock only about six or seven feet from where I stood. Then I realised that it was a mermaid. She was no grey seal; she was a real mermaid — a bonnie lassie, clear in complexion. Her hair was reddish-yellow and curly; and she had a wreath of seaweed round her neck. She had greenish-blue eyes and arched eyebrows, and she stared at me with a kind of frightened expression. She had a dark yellowish body the colour of the yellow sands on the sea-shore. Like myself, she also got a fright. She never moved, not even her wee short arms, as she reclined amid the noise of the surf with her fish-like tail dangling over the side of the rock. She did not speak.

"I sensed the situation right away. She could not move until the high tide came. She was marooned upon the rock on which she rested. She was in an angry mood — angry because I had discovered her, and she was frightened too! It is all very difficult to describe; but she was the size of an ordinary human being, with the same features; but she had an arched back. She was very beautiful.

"For minutes only, the mermaid and I gazed at one another. Then, realising that what I saw was supernormal, I took to my heels in terror. What I had seen, coupled with the remembrance of my dog's howls, frightened me, and I followed after my dog in trembling fear of that maiden of the sea."

Sandy Gunn concluded his statement by saying: "You may all scoff at me as much as you choose; but I saw a real mermaid, and I will not depart from my story for any man on earth. What I saw was real. I actually encountered a mermaid."

Alexander Gunn, who was a highly respected small landholder on the Kinlochbervie estate, died at Balchrick in December, 1944.

The Mermaid of Loch Inchard

In June, 1939, while fishing from a boat on Loch Inchard, a lady staying at Garbet Hotel, Kinlochbervie, suddenly noticed what she took to be a bunch of yellow seaweed, rise to the surface of the water a few feet in front of her, while the boat she was in was peacefully drifting off Achriesgill Bay. To her surprise, the 'sea tangle' turned round in the water, revealing a beautiful face. It was not seaweed at all, but fair golden hair out of which peered a lovely face with blue eyes and delicate colouring. The lady in the rowing boat was tongue-tied with astonishment, and when she finally managed to direct her friends' attention to the object in the water, the mermaid sank from view, and her tail broke the surface of the water before she disappeared into the inky depths. When the lady mentioned the matter to her gillie, he told her that this mermaid had often been seen floating in Loch Inchard, or lying on the rocks by the shore. The mermaid had never spoken to anyone, and had never done any harm; but for all that, the local people were afraid of her as something 'not canny.'

The Man in the Surf

Some years ago a fisherman named Alexander Mackay was preparing his evening meal one autumn night inside the old hut at Port Mor, Sutherland, when he heard the sound of a hoarse voice. Thinking someone might be in distress, he lit his lantern and went outside to investigate. Peering in the direction of the sound, he beheld in the rays from his lamp a creature which resembled a human being staring at him from the top of a boulder amid the surf of the high tide. As he approached, he saw a man with swarthy face, short curly hair, small eyes, a flat nose, a large mouth and exceptionally long arms. The merman gazed at him fixedly for a moment or two before slipping off the rock into the sea. Mackay realised that he was looking at no ordinary person, for, as the strange figure turned round in the water before diving from sight, he could see that the hairy body tapered into a fish-tail. The merman reappeared a short distance away along with what he took to be a mermaid. Alarmed at what he had seen, the fisherman rushed back to the hut with all speed, as he believed that he had beheld the spirits of his ancestors, as a sept of the Clan Mackay claims descent from a mermaid.

In the superstitious belief of the North, seals held a far higher place than any other of the lower animals. They were believed to have a mysterious connection with the human race, and to have the power of assuming human form and faculties. Near Sheigra there are some rocks much frequented by seals, and one Christmas morning a local crofter saw a 'selchie' (seal) asleep on one of the ledges. Coming up to it, he shot it, took the carcase home, skinned it and boiled part of it for oil. Shortly afterwards his only cow died, and the crofter attributed this to his shooting of the seal. Next Christmas morning, the same man was walking near the shore when he saw another 'selchie' lying in the same position fast asleep. This time, however, he did not shoot, but went home immediately lest he should be tempted to kill this one and so bring more misfortune on himself, so great was his belief that the death of his cow had been a judgment on him.

A Reay Mermaid

On January 12, 1809, a daughter of the Rev. David Mackay, minister of Reay, Caithness, was walking along the sea-shore at Reay, when she observed three people on a rock nearby, showing signs of terror and astonishment at something in the water. On approaching, she distinguished that the object of their wonder was a face resembling the human countenance, which appeared floating on the surface of the water. The face, throat and arms were all she observed.

The sea at that level was running very high, and as the waves advanced, the mermaid sank gently under them, but afterwards reappeared. The face was plump and round, the eyes and nose were small; the former were of light grey colour; the mouth was large, the jawbone appeared straight, which caused the face to look small; the hand was round and the hair thick and long, and of a green oily colour, which appeared troublesome to her. The arms were frequently extended over her head to ward off a bird which hovered above. No hair or scales were observed, and the smoothness of the skin, which was white, was discernible.

Cnoc na Cnoimh

Nearly eight hundred years ago, a terrible scourge fell upon the fertile valley of the Cassley, in Sutherland. A fierce monster had taken up its abode in a hole on the east side of a hill in the vicinity, and no living thing was safe from its fury. In shape, the monster was like a huge worm, and if it had ventured out into the open, people might have learned how to avoid it, for worms are not as a rule noted for their speed of movement. But this monster's power lay in its venomous breath, which poisoned all that came within reach of its rapacious jaws. As a rule the worm lay hidden in its hole, breathing out noxious vapour like the smoke from a volcano. So powerful was its breath, that it hung over the countryside for miles, bringing certain destruction to all living things. The valley soon became desolate, and the people of the district fled from their houses.

At intervals, the worm left its lair and crawled slowly to the summit of the hill, winding its sinuous length round and round; and on these occasions, it used to lie as if surveying the scene of desolation round about with the greatest satisfaction. The hole in which the monster lived came to be called *"Toll na Cnoimh"* (Worm's Hole), and the hill round which it coiled itself *"Cnoc na Cnoimh"* (Worm's Hill).

William the Lion, King of Scotland, heard of the misfortune which had befallen this part of his realm, and offered a large reward to anyone who would slay the monster. But none of his knights was brave enough to attempt such a perilous task, and when no one came to their rescue the country folk lost heart, for it seemed as though they would have to go on living in fear all their lives. At last a rough-and-ready farmer from the Kyle of Sutherland — Hector Gunn by name — came forward and said that although he was a plain man he would try to slay the beast and rid the countryside of it for good and all. He mounted his horse and rode till he came to within a few miles of *"Cnoc na Cnoimh."* He asked the people where the Worm's Hole was; but they answered that the monster was not in the hole that day, but had crawled up the side of the hill and lay sunning itself on the top as if like *"an Diabhull"* (the Evil One) he thought that all the world was his.

The farmer then wheeled his horse round and rode straight for the hill. He had with him a broadsword with which to sever the creature's head; but he soon found that this would not avail him at all, for before he came near to the foot of the hill, he felt the worm's poisonous breath coming towards him in waves of fetid heat, and became so weak and faint that he could go no further. He returned crestfallen to where the pople were waiting for him, and great were their lamentations on seeing his dejected mien, for he had gone out full of confidence that he would deliver them from the scourge. "It is a good thing that the worm was asleep," they said, "or else Hector Gunn would have been utterly consumed."

Hector Gunn did not allow himself to be beaten by a worm, not even by one with such unearthly powers as this. When he had recovered somewhat from his faintness, he borrowed a seven-ell-long spear, and asked the astonished villagers if they had any pitch. They said that they had, and he ordered them to boil some of it in a pot. He then went on to the moor and cut a great divot of peat. He thrust the end of the long spear through the peat, and dipped it in the boiling pitch. With this strange weapon in his hand, he mounted his horse once more and rode towards *"Cnoc na Cnoimh."* The country people followed at a distance, wondering. As soon as Hector Gunn came near the monster and it opened its mouth to suck him in with its poisonous breath, he held out the spear with the reeking peat at the end, and the wind blew the fumes right into the worm's face. So strange and pungent was the smoke that the creature was almost suffocated, and drew its breath, and wound itself tighter and tighter round the hill in its agony.

Hector rode nearer and nearer, till he was on a level with

He thrust the burning peat down its throat

the monster, then with one quick movement he thrust the burning peat down its throat and held it there until the fearsome creature died.

Thus was the valley of Cassley delivered from the worm; and William the Lion rewarded Hector Gunn with gifts of land and money. And — to this day, men may go to "*Cnoc na Cnoimh*" and see traces of this old story in the spiral indentations said to have been made on the hillside by the worm as its coils tightened in its death throes.

Water-kelpies

An old pamphlet, dated 1823, refers to water-kelpies as follows: — "In the former and darker ages of the world, when people had not half the wit and sagacity they now possess, and when, consequently, they were much more easily duped by such designing agents, the 'Ech Usique', or water-horse, as the kelpie is commonly called, was a well-known character in these countries. The kelpie was an infernal agent, retained in the service and pay of Satan, who granted him a commission to execute such services as appeared profitable to his interest. He was an amphibious character, and generally took up his residence in lochs and pools, bordering on public roads and other situations most convenient for his professional calling.

The likeness of a fine steed was a favourite disguise

His commission consisted in the destruction of human beings, without affording them time to prepare for their immortal interests, and thus endeavour to send their souls to his master, while he, the kelpie, enjoyed the body. However, he had no authority to touch a human being of his own free accord, unless the latter was the aggressor. In order, therefore, to delude public travellers and others to their destruction, it was the common practice of the kelpie to assume the most fascinating form, and assimilate himself to that likeness, which he supposed most congenial to the inclinations of his intended victim.

The likeness of a fine riding steed was his favourite disguise. Decked out in the most splendid riding accoutrements, the perfidious kelpie would place himself in the weary traveller's way, and graze by the road-side with all the seeming innocence and simplicity in the world .... But this horse knew better what he was about; he was as calm and peaceable as a lamb, until his victim was once fairly mounted on his back; with a fiend-like yell he would then announce his triumph, and plunging headlong with his woe-struck rider into an adjacent pool, enjoy him for his repast."

Loch A'Garbh Bhaid Beag

This story was told by John Falconer, Achlyness, Sutherland.

One afternoon in the autumn of 1938, Mary Falconer, a woman of Achlyness in West Sutherland, was taking a short cut with a companion through the hills to Ardchullin with some venison in a sack slung over her shoulder.

On nearing Loch Garget Beag, she noticed a number of ponies grazing by the loch-side. Thinking that one of the beasts — a white one — was her next-door-neighbour's sheltie, and that she would make use of it for carrying her heavy load on its back the rest of the journey to Rhiconich, she walked towards the animal.

As she came within a few feet of it, however, she discovered that it was a much larger pony than her neighbour's, and to her astonishment, she saw round its neck, entangled with its mane, a cluster of water weeds.

The eyes of the animal and the woman met; and in that instant she sensed that she was looking on an "*each uisge*" and on no ordinary beast.

To her amazement, there and then the whole group of about thirteen ponies, on noticing her, galloped to the edge of the water, and plunging into the loch, sank below the surface in front of her eyes.

Her companion corroborated her story in every particular.

The people of Kinlochbervie and district are firmly convinced that Loch Garbet Beag houses in its depths not one water-horse, but a whole herd.

(Mary Falconer was well known locally as a "Seer." There was hardly a funeral in the district that she did not forecast. Not only did she "see" funerals before they took place; but counted the number of conveyances and recognised the mourners. On one occasion, she saw the long grass and bracken sway beneath the pall-bearers' feet as they carried the coffin — long before the actual death occurred.)

The creature of Loch Voshmaid

Told by George Ross, Corriemulzie, Sutherland.

During the time of the following incident I was head stalker to the late Sir Samuel Scott. One day, a friend of mine (a guest of Sir Samuel) went to Loch Voshnaid in North Harris — known in the district as "The Enchanted Lochan." He took with him a new fly which he stated possessed supernatural powers. He had no luck that day, but had a great story to tell round the dinner table that night.

"As my new fly failed to move a fish," he said, "I resolved to try the worm from off a steep bank at a corner of the loch. For a long time nothing happened. Then all of a sudden, I got a terrific tug and my rod bent nearly double! As I proceeded to haul in my line, the head of a huge and grotesque creature appeared in front of me and its tail lashed out on the surface about a quarter of a mile away, near the bank on the opposite side of the loch. This monster ran out every foot of line from my reel, and just as I was being drawn into the water after my rod, I heard the sound of fairy bagpipes. A door opened in the hillside opposite, and a troop of 'Wee Folk' trailed the whole fish, tail first, into a hole in the rocks. Then my line snapped, the door closed and my fish was gone! I could still hear the pipes playing underneath the ground as I packed up."

The monster of Strathhalladale

Many years ago, a girl in a Caithness parish incurred the wrath of a local "wise woman", who pronounced on her a terrible "*guidhe*" (curse).

Like Titania in "A Midsummer Night's Dream", she was put under a "*geas*" (spell) to love a monster. The girl laughed at the old woman, and soon forgot the curse.

When she grew to womanhood, she married a man from Strathmore, and on their wedding day he was bringing her from Strathhalladale to his home when they were overtaken on the moor by a dense mist. They lost their way, and came upon a lonely bothy in which they took shelter for the night. They contrived to light a fire, and were stitting by it when without annoucement or salutation a strange being entered the bothy — in form like a handsome young man; but goat-bearded, goat-faced and with the tail of a horse.

"Who is to have this woman?" asked the monster. "Who," said the man, "but he to whom she belongs." To this the satyr replied, "Let us fight for her." Then they began to fight, and under the man's hard blows the monster was soon lying on the ground.

Then an amazing thing happened. His wife, hitherto so gentle, rushed to the help of the monster, and turned on her husband with the fury of a demon. Horror-struck at her disloyalty, and unable to strike a woman, he realised that his only alternative was flight, and made for home with a heavy heart.

After a few days his wife appeared at Strathmore, apparently cured of her infatuation; but in due course she had a son who resembled the monster, especially in possession of a tail.

This story, with a different setting, is given as authentic by the late Dr Alexander McBain in a paper delivered to the Gaelic Society of Inverness in 1888. Descendants of the son, each distinguished by the possession of a tail, are said to be still alive, "not a hundred miles from Bonar Bridge."

Visitor from the sea

If on a Highland beach you should come across the belongings of a sailor washed ashore from a wreck, leave them lying where they are. Should you pick them up the chances are that the shade of the dead owner will come to ask you for them back.

One day at Sheigra in Kinlochbervie a crofter picked up the belongings of a sailor drowned off the coast nearby. Some nights later a strange man inexplicably appeared in his croft. He was dressed as a sailor and after roaming about the room he disappeared. The following night he came again and then on several succcessive nights, each time staying a little longer than before. In time he began to get obstreperous and started upsetting the furniture.

The crofter became very alarmed and summoned the minister, who advised that the ghost be asked what it was he wanted. The crofter was afraid because of the belief that to converse with a spirit ensured death within a year. Finally he plucked up courage and spoke to the phantom who replied in Gaelic. Crofter and ghost then walked out of the croft together and went down to the sea-shore where the spirit walked into the water and slowly dissolved into mist. The crofter is still alive today. He will not tell what words passed between them but says only that the sailor went back to the sea satisfied and has not reappeared since.

The swaying bed

This story was told by the late Mr Donald Macleod of Kinlochbervie. Some years ago he was on holiday in Sutherland and asked for a room in a cottage opposite Gordonbush, Brora. As he was falling asleep he felt a chill wind blowing through the room and sensed the presence of something evil. After a few minutes he felt his bed slowly sinking down at the top left-hand corner and swaying as though the leg had been removed. He was petrified with fear and hid his head under the blankets. Before long he felt his pillow begin to wriggle beneath his head. Mustering all his courage he seized his Bible from the bedside table and sprang into the middle of the room. The door which he had locked closed with a loud bang. He recited the Lord's Prayer and gradually everything became quiet. Several other visitors have had similar experiences in this room, although as far as is known no tragedy is associated with it.

The green lady of Barrogil

The unhappy girl falls to her death

There is a room in the tower of Barrogil Castle, Caithness, right at the top. Looking from the outside this room had a dummy window painted on the stonework, while inside you can see that the window has been walled up. Thereby hangs a tragic story. The bedroom is known as "Lady Fanny's room" owing to some confusion by the historians in linking Lady Fanny Sinclair, sister of the 19th Earl of Caithness and the last to live at Barrogil, with the daughter of a much earlier Earl, the fifth.

Four hundred years ago, this daughter of the Sinclair family, so the story goes, fell desperately in love with a young ploughman who worked the fields of Barrogil Farm, next door. Vowing that he would soon put a stop to the romance, the Earl locked his daughter in the top room of the tower. Discovering that she was spending her days gazing through the window at her lover as he worked in the fields, the Earl vowed he would stop that also, and bricked up the window, whereupon the unhappy girl threw herself from the remaining window to her death in the courtyard below.

No one knows if the story is true, or whether the Earl's daughter still appears in the castle as "The Green Lady". Barrogil is now the Scottish home of the Queen Mother, and known as the Castle of Mey. Though the Queen Mother knows the story, she is not perturbed. Neither she nor any member of the staff has ever seen The Green Lady.

A Strath Oykell vision

One New Year's Eve, many years ago, a young shepherd in Corriemulzie went to Oykell Bridge, Sutherland, the nearest hamlet — some eight miles distant — to call on some friends.

After paying his respects at Oykell Bridge, he called later on that evening at a crofter's house two miles up the Strath, where he spent some hours celebrating. The weather had been stormy and a previous fall of snow had slightly thawed and

The shepherd walked confidently down the icy road

frozen. The main road was coated with ice to such an extent that it was practically impossible to walk along it, and people were forced on the verge of the adjoining hillside.

About ten o'clock the following morning, New Year's Day, a farmer went out to feed his cattle with his eldest son, a lad of ten or eleven. As they were passing the end of a cart-shed furthest away from the road, they noticed a figure, who they immediately recognised, walking rapidly down the hill. They both remarked on his sure grip on the ice.

The shepherd walked quickly and confidently down the icy road, and the farmer's little boy, rather curious, ran to the end of the building to see what fittings he had on his boots.

When the boy got there, the young shepherd had vanished. Later in the day, a message arrived from the shepherd's croft to say that he had not returned the previous night. A search party was sent out, and his footprints were followed in the snow where he had taken a short cut over the rocks on his way home. There the searchers found where he had slipped over a boulder and had been badly injured. He had crawled in the snow to where his dead body was found, and afterwards carried home.

A doctor was called and gave the approximate time of death as between nine and ten o'clock that day — the time when the farmer and his son "saw" the figure walking down the hill.

The Meikle Ferry tragedy

On a market day in Tain in the year 1809, several Sutherland crofters and Sheriff MacCulloch of Dornoch, crossed over in the ferry-boat. Towards evening, the shore on the Ross-shire side towards Meikle Ferry was crowded with those going home, and far too many climbed into the boat. It was a dead calm and

The dead man told where his body lay

the heavily laden vessel pushed off from the land; but when it had nearly reached the middle, and the deepest part of the water, it lurched over on its side. The water rushed in, and all the occupants were thrown overboard.

About seventy people were drowned, and the sea gave up its dead one by one, until only the Sheriff's body remained below the water. A friend of MacCulloch's was deeply affected by his death, and had a dream in which the dead man appeared by his bedside, spoke of his sudden death, and described where his body lay. He added that the fish seemed to have been restrained from touching his body, which would be found unmutilated. The dream was fulfilled in every particular.

The death of the Duke of Sutherland

In 1892, the Duke and Duchess of Sutherland were not at the Northern Meeting Games at Inverness the first day; but as nothing was known to be wrong, were expected from Dunrobin Castle on the second.

There was in the town a young police officer who saw "*Sealladh*" (visions). On the night of the first day of the Games, this man dreamt that he was at the Gathering, and that while there he was handed a telegram to the effect that the Duke had died at 10.30 pm the night before. He woke trembling and related his dream to his family, who were more annoyed than credulous.

As the policeman was trying to compose himself again, the telephone rang. It was the Chief Constable of Inverness — with the news that the Duke of Sutherland had died the previous evening at 10.30 o'clock.

Signs of conflict

The late Angus Morrison, who lived in a lonely cottage at Sheigra, near Cape Wrath, almost sixty miles from the nearest railway station, was an old sailor-fisherman. He wore one gold earring — after the old custom in certain districts in the North of Scotland — to help to pay for the cost of burial, should the wearer be drowned at sea and his body washed ashore.

Some fifty-five years ago, Angus Morrison told his friends how he frequently heard the noise of engines running at the top of a certain hill above his croft. He was insistent, despite their scepticism, and asserted that he often heard the sound at night as well as through the day. There was no road to the place indicated, far less a railway line. During the Second World War, a radar station was set up on the exact spot he had indicated. He had only heard the sound of its engines a few years in advance.

Night lights

Occasionally at night a strange and unaccountable light is seen out at sea off the west coast of Sutherland. The local people call it "*Teine*" (fire). This light, or fire, has been observed travelling at considerable speed, and is believed to foretell calamity or disaster. Seen from the Kinlochbervie shore it is termed "The Assynt Light" *(Teine Assynt)* and viewed from the Assynt coast it is known as "The Mackay's Light" *(Solus MhicAoidh)*. The cause of this peculiar phenomenon still remains a mystery; but at times, this midnight fire which sweeps the Minch is very bright.

On winter nights, when there is peace on sea and land, the

"Fir-chlisneach" (Nimble Men, or Merry Dancers), come forth to dance in the northern sky. Such is the poetic explanation given by the romantically-minded Celt of the scientific phenomenon known as the "Aurora Borealis", those

"Fearful lights that never beacon
Save when Kings or heroes die."

Another name for the Northern Lights is "The Streamers", and it is said that when they have a battle among themselves, as often happens, the blood of the wounded falls to the earth and becomes congealed in the form of "blood-stones", called in the Hebrides *"Fuil siochaire"* (elf's blood).

A prophecy of war

Some seventy years ago, there lived at Newton Moss, near Wick, an old woman called Morag Guinne (Sarah Gunn). Her appearance was not prepossessing; she had a wrinkled face like tough leather, small piercing eyes, a hooked nose, and grey hair falling over her bony shoulders and sprouting from her pointed chin. She was known to be a *"taibhsear,"* and was reputed to be a witch also. She used to sit on a three-legged stool inside her cottage and draw cabalistic designs with her broom-handle on the flagstones, from which she prophesied (for a monetary consideration) "the shape of things to come." Her *"fios nam fadh"* (foreknowledge) seemed to be confined to dark and terrible happenings; and few who visited her cottage at dead of night to consult her, dared speak of what they had heard within its walls.

On one occasion, two anglers who happened to pass her cottage at dusk decided to ask for a cup of tea. The atmosphere inside the cottage was anything but friendly. After much haggling, the old woman agreed to make tea for them;

The 'witch' makes a grim prediction

but as she made it she muttered to herself in sinister monotones about trials and tribulations which would come upon the countryside. This got on the nerves of one of the anglers, who tried to divert the old woman's attention by some jocular remark. Disregard of her prophecies angered her, however, and drawing herself up she cursed him. *"Ruith nah-Aoin' ort, deire nan seachd Sathurn' ort, agus na meal thusa do shlainte!"* she shrieked (The hurry of Friday be on you, the end of the seven Saturdays be upon you, and may you not enjoy your health!), and then went on to say, "I am an old woman, and near to death. Before I die, in one month's time, there will be increasing disquietude on the earth; and twenty years from now there will be mourning in my land, when many coffins will be borne eastward to the burying-ground in solemn procession. I 'see' many a funeral, at the rate of five or more a day, of victims washed up on yonder shore!"

In about a month's time, Sarah Gunn died; and twenty years later (1940) the Second World War started, and, just as she had foretold, corpses were being daily washed ashore from vessels wrecked off the Caithness coast.

A death warning

A girl from Kinlochbervie, who possessed the gift of "The Sight" (Second Sight), was for some years house-keeper to a laird who lived in a lodge overlooking Badcall Bay, near Scourie, Sutherland. One afternoon in early spring, she saw her master drive away in his car. A short time afterwards, for no accountable reason, she began to feel very depressed, and sensed a sort of indescribable evil foreboding, which she tried hard to shake off, but could not. As she was cooking lunch, she was startled to hear footfalls in the house. Feeling very uneasy, for she was quite alone, she hurried into the hall, but found no one there, but she heard heavy footsteps ascending the upper portion of the stair. She distinctly heard her master's bedroom door open and a noise as if several persons were scuffling about in his room above. The room, however, was quite empty, and just the way her master had left it. Believing that she was imagining things, she returned to the kitchen.

All of a sudden a car drove up to the lodge. Answering a knock at the front door, she saw the local police officer, who informed her that he had received a telephone call to inform him that the laird had been drowned in a roadside lochan while attempting to rescue a lamb which had fallen into the water, and that he was on his way down in the police car to the scene of the accident. Having broken the tragic news, the police officer immediately departed. A short while afterwards, the laird's car arrived at the house with some people inside it and they carried the dead man up the stairs to his bedroom. The footsteps which she heard ascending the stairs with the corpse to the

They carried the laird upstairs

room above, corresponded exactly to the identical shuffling footfalls which she had heard about an hour previously. What actually had happened was that, seeing a lamb struggling in the water by the roadside, the laird threw off his kilt and plunged into the loch in an endeavour to rescue the animal; but the shock of the icy water proved too much for him and he died.

The curse of Kylesku

Many years ago, after a wreck, a keg of whisky was washed ashore at Kerrachar Bay in Loch Cairnbawn. The cask was discovered by a local fisherman nicknamed *"Tordeas"* who carried it into the old ferryhouse (now the Kylesku Hotel).

After depositing the cask in an upstairs room on the west side of the inn (access is gained by a wooden loft ladder) he invited some of his friends to come and share the contents with him.

During the orgy which followed, a "Seer" who was present prophesied a great calamity; but he was ridiculed by the other men. A drunken argument followed, and so heated did it become that "Tordeas" protested that the hour was drawing near to the Lord's Day.

His son, losing his temper, came to grips with his father and flung him headlong down the stairs. The fall broke his neck, and he died screaming in agony: "My son, I shall return to have my revenge!"

The son was found drowned on the shores of Loch Glencoul a few weeks later. Tordeas's revenge holds good to this day, for each year at midnight, on the anniversary of the occurrence, his ghost is said to appear at the entrance to the hotel "snuggery" below the loft ladder leading up to the upstairs room. The room itself has remained unused to the present day.

Note — Several local people have encountered the ghost, and one guest who saw it was the late Professor C M Joad, of BBC radio fame, who stayed at the Kylesku Ferry Inn in the Fifties.

The son's terrible crime

Curing the Murrain

Distempers among cattle were formerly very common in Caithness; now, however, improved management and draining has greatly diminished cattle diseases. The murrain, or, as it was locally called, 'the hasty,' because the cattle died very soon after being attacked by it, was one of the most common diseases; so common and dreaded that it appears in county histories that many old women, reputed to have the power of curing the murrain, made considerable sums by the exercise of their deceptive trade. The cure was supposed to be effected by a need-fire, and the manner of raising this is thus recorded:

"Upon any small island where the stream of a river or burn runs on each side, a circular booth was erected of stone or turf, in which a semi-circular or highland 'couple' of birch, or other hard wood, was set; and a roof constructed upon it. A straight pole was set up in the centre of this building, the upper end being fixed by a wooden pin to the top of the couple, and the lower end in an oblong trunk in the earth or floor; and lastly, another pole was set across horizontally, having both ends tapered, one end of which was supported in a hole in the side of the perpendicular pole, and the other in a similar hole in the couple leg.

"The horizontal stick was called the auger, having four short arms or levers fixed in its centre, to work it by; the building having been thus finished, as many men as could be collected in the vicinity (being divested of all kinds of metal in their clothes) would set to work with the said auger, two after two, constantly turning it round by the arms or levers, and others occasionally driving wedges of wood or stone behind the lower end of the upright pole, so as to press it the more on the end of the auger; by this constant friction and pressure, the ends of the auger would take fire, from which a fire would be instantly kindled, and thus the need-fire would be accomplished. The fire in the farmer's house was now quenched with water, a fire kindled from this need-fire, both in the farm house and offices, and the cattle brought in to feel the smoke of this new and sacred fire, which preserved them from dying of the murrain. In order to expedite the raising of this need-fire, several gimlet holes in the ends of the auger were previously filled with gunpowder and tinder."

This superstitious performance was probably a vestige of the raising of the sacred fire of the Druids annually on May-day. The ceremony was performed in Ireland as well as in Scotland, and May 1 is still called in Gaelic *La Bealltuinn* — the day of Baal's fire, or that dedicated to Baal, or the sun. The belief in the efficacy of the need-fire has died, but in more recent times it appears that in certain districts in Scotland a superstitious dislike was entertained against winnowing machines, because they were supposed to interfere with the elements.

The Two-headed Dog of Kildonan

At the bottom of a deep pool near Kildonan, Sutherland, there was said to be a priceless pot of gold. The local people believed that a two-headed dog lived there and guarded the treasure.

A farmer, however, decided to drain the pool and this he did till only a big hole remained in the ground. As the dog did not show itself, and there was no trace of the treasure, the farmer, feeling tired, went home to bed.

About midnight a hideous howling woke him. Looking outside, he beheld the two-headed dog. He was terrified. Each evening the dog paid him a visit, and this did not cease until the farmer had filled up the hole he had made and allowed the water to cover it again.

The Old Manse of Lairg

The Rev Thomas Mackay, who was minister of Lairg, Sutherland, and who, during his lifetime, usually wore full clerical dress (that of a bishop), died in August, 1803. On a fine summer day in 1826 two young girls were sitting in the manse dining-room, when they heard a step advancing to the door. The door opened, and there stood a thin, venerable old man, dressed in black, with knee breeches and buckles, black silk stockings and shoes with buckles. He looked closely all round the room, and then walked out. One of the girls ran upstairs and told the minister, then in the manse, that a very old minister had come and was looking for him. The minister hurried down and looked for his visitor, but in vain. The manse is so placed that every object can be seen for a quarter of a mile around, but not a trace of the visitor was visible. The old people, who heard the girls describe the old man they had seen, recognised the Rev Thomas Mackay from their description. According to authentic information, not so long ago two local poachers, while at work during the hours of darkness outside the Old Manse, became so terrified on account of the unearthly sounds which they heard issuing from within the building, that they abandoned their gear and fled in terror back to the village.

The Laird and the Witches

The last execution of a witch in Scotland took place in Sutherland, in 1772; but the belief of the people after the repeal of the laws demanding the punishment of witches and warlocks, was for a long time as strong as it was at that date. I gleaned the following narrative, while on a visit to Drumbeg,

Sutherland, from a somewhat soiled handwritten manuscript dated 1887, and said to be by a former factor on the Assynt estate.

About two centuries ago there lived in the hamlet of Drumbeg, in the parish of Assynt, Sutherland, an old woman and her daughter renowned for their many cantrips. Tradition leaves the name of the old Hecate unrevealed, but her daughter's name was Mor Bhan or White Sarah. They were the plague of the countryside. Everyone shunned them as the cholera. One of the lairds of Assynt was very knowledgeable about the witches of his time, and especially with the mother of Mor Bhan. He always used to harass them, and for revenge they made a *corp creadha*, or a clay image for him. He had been a soldier and had one of his ears shot off in the wars. About the time the witches were making the clay corpse for him he was taken very ill, and ordered one of his retainers to go to Lochinver and consult a famous local 'lighiche' or healer. The messenger had a very long and tiresome walk across the hills, bogs and moors of Upper Assynt. And worse than all it was a very rough night.

Half-way between Inchnadamph and Aultnacealgach he heard somebody saying in a greeting voice: "We'll manage ye, Donald. We'll manage ye. We'll take ye." He looked and saw to his great astonishment two witches sitting in the path before him. They were moulding an image of clay, which was all stuck over with pins, but somehow or other they could not get the ear to stick on the image. They did not know that the laird was minus the ear, and so the treacherous beldams were helpless. The retainer understood at a glance that this was a 'clay corpse' which the witches were making for the laird, his master, and which accounted for his illness. He also recognised Mor Bhan's mother, but not the other witch.

He waited for a few minutes without taking any proceeding to discomfit their satanic plan, to see what further steps they would take. Their jargon was mostly unintelligible to him as they attempted fruitlessly to mould the ear to the image, but he could understand a few words, such as expressions of surprise and annoyance, when they would fail in their undertaking.

"We can never get the ear on him, ochone! ochone! ochone!" and then, when they would think they were successful, they would say, "We'll manage ye yet, Donald. Ha! Ha! Ha!" The retainer being a strong man, in fact he was a second Hercules, and as agile as an Olympian runner, waited no longer, but rushed at them and knocked them over.

He then seized the image and ran with it home to his master, for, being witches, they could not cross the running water of the burn, which was in close proximity to them, else they would lose their witchcraft. When the retainer reached the laird's house he took the image up to the chamber where his master lay, and gave it to him. The image was covered all over with pins, and in its very heart there was a miniature cup full of water. When the water would run through the small holes in the cup it was supposed the victim would immediately die.

The laird first drew out a large pin from the side of the cup. In a minute he was greatly relieved. They then took out the other pins, one after the other, each giving him greater relief, till at last, when they were all removed, he was quite well.

The following night the laird sent a servant to Dornoch on an errand in connection with the witches. He wanted a warrant for their apprehension. Tha man rather hung back as it was a wild and stormy night, and he would have to cross a very mischancy ford, which was sometimes impassable. MacLeod, on noticing his hesitancy, roared out to him: "Take the grey horse, and the devil himself will not stop you." He took it with some misgivings and rode into the darkness. On reaching the ford he found his bridle seized by two witches, one on each side. The retainer in a bold voice said: "I have been waiting to see you this long time." The witches retorted: "And we are very glad to see you. All you have to do is sign your name in blood in this parchment book in the name of the devil."

The retainer made no more ado, but took the pen, pricked himself till the blood came, then laying the book open on the saddle before him, was about to write, when all at once he gave the grey a slap behind with his open hand. Up the grey sprang far into the air, and threw down both witches into the water. The grey then sprang round, amidst the imprecations of the witches, and sped home like the wind. The man held the book tight under his arm. He was soon at his master's house, and gave him the book. In it the laird saw the names of all the witches in Sutherland, chief among whom was Mor Bhan's mother.

The laird, on the ensuing Sabbath, proclaimed in the kirk that if any harm was done to him or his he would know who had done it, and punish accordingly. So no harm was ever done him afterwards. However, he ordered Mor Bhan's mother to be arrested, and she was taken as a prisoner to Dornoch.

For a whole year she neither ate, drank, nor spoke, but remained leaning on her cuigeal or distaff. When at last nobody could make her speak, a young minister said: "I am sure I can." So he went to Dornoch, but what he said to her is not known. However, he made her speak, and the first words she said were: "Thou hast deceived me, O devil, saying that no one born of living woman could ever make me speak. Ochone! ochone! ochone!"

"Oh, no! he has not deceived you," said the young minister, "for my mother died just before I was born on an island in Loch Ness." So saying, he kicked away her distaff, and she fell to the ground, a heap of dust.

Black-haired Currie

Many years ago the beautiful daughter of the then Laird of Glendhu in Sutherland fell in love with a fierce sea-captain of the name of Currie, who belonged to Gairloch in Ross-shire. According to the legend, Currie's ship — a fishing vessel — hit a rock somewhere near Kylescu on her way into Loch Glendhu, but the skipper managed to run her aground and save the crew. It was while waiting there for repairs that he made the acquaintance of the laird's daughter, and their friendship quickly ripened into love. Before Currie left Loch Glendhu for far-away ports, she had promised to wait for him, and he swore to be true to her and to marry her next time he came back on his ship to Kylescu. They arranged to correspond regularly when he was away.

Sir John Mackenzie of Achmore, Assynt, was also seeking the girl's hand in marriage, and although she had no fancy at all for Sir John, her father was very anxious that she should marry him, and did his utmost to make her forget her seaman lover. The laird in those days had certain powers over the mails, and was able to intercept all letters between Currie and his daughter, so that she despaired of ever seeing him again. In her soreness of heart, she is said to have sung a song called 'Black-haired Currie of the Rope,' which is still popular in the district.

At last, however, she yielded to her father's persuasions and married Sir John. Some time afterwards, Currie came back to Loch Glendhu and was told about the grand marriage of the laird's daughter. Furious with anger, and determined to prove that he at least had been faithful, he shouldered his gun and set off for Achmore. When Sir John saw him approach, he fled in seeming terror to the hills. Currie spent all that day and the next night with his former sweetheart, then set off for Kylescu.

Knowing that now she could never be his, he tried to drink himself into a state of oblivion at Kylescu Inn, and being in a fuddled condition as he left for the shore, did not notice Sir John, who having only feigned terror, had concealed himself until Currie left Achmore and had followed him to Kylescu. Sir John shot him through the heart as he was leaving the inn, dragged the body up to Lochan Dubh by the road to Kylescu Post Office, and dumped the remains into the lochan (later the small reservoir to supply Kylescu Hotel.with water).

He then returned to Achmore, where, after shooting his

faithless wife, he turned the gun on himself. The ghost of the murdered skipper is still said to haunt Lochan Dubh; and those who have passed by Achmore late at night when the moon is full declare that they have seen the pale wraith of the unhappy bride, and have heard the strains of her plaintive song, 'Currie Dubh Nan Ropa.'

The Fisherman's Boots

A tremendous storm had swept the north-west coast of Sutherland for about thirty-six hours, during which the beach at Oldshoremore, near Kinlochbervie, had been piled high with seaweed, flotsam and jetsam. After the tempest had subsided, next morning, a local crofter, gathering scraps of wood along high-water mark, noticed a fine pair of seaman's thigh boots protruding from a large cluster of seaweed, and thinking that someone — probably one of his neighbours — had covered himself over with seaweed in order to play a practical joke on him, he sought a reprisal. So seizing hold of both boots by their respective soles, he shouted out, as he started to haul them from the kelp: "Faodaidh t-anam a bhi ann an ifrinn ach tha do bhrogan agamsa" ("Your soul may be in hell, but I've got your boots").

To his amazement, he discovered that the boots were heavy with the weight of human limbs, and as he continued to pull, the grisly body of a dead sailor slowly came into view from underneath the sea wrack. The corpse was chill and ghastly. A strange feeling crept over the crofter as his envious eyes focused on the fine sea boots. After all, this was a wonderful opportunity. Boots were boots, and expensive, and these were the best he had ever seen. With difficulty he first removed one sea boot and then the other from off the dead man's limbs, and carried them home with him and buried them under a pile of hay in an outhouse next to his croft, before informing his wife and the police that a dead sailor had been washed up on the beach.

After the usual preliminaries had been attended to and the police satisfied, the unidentified seaman was laid to rest in the nearby churchyard, down the road, near the sea. The whole affair was soon forgotten until, one day, the crofter found his wife pale and distressed. She whispered: "I happened to go into the hay shed about an hour ago to look for stray hen eggs, when a very strange thing happened. I overheard a voice, a man's voice. It had an English accent. I could see no one."

"Go on," said the crofter, also turning white. "What else?" His wife continued: "Well, it was rather strange. I know it sounds foolish, but I seemed to see the hay move at the far corner of the shed, as if slightly ruffled by the breeze, and the voice seemed to gasp out, in a sort of whisper, something about calling tonight for a pair of boots."

"My God!" moaned her husband. "What else did the thing say?"

"Well, John," she answered, "before I had time to leave the shed to see if someone from outside was speaking to me, whatever it was, the voice told me that *you* knew where the boots were, and that he would not have far to come to collect them, for he would only require to walk up the pathway from the churchyard by the sea-shore."

The Maiden of the Fall

When in flood, Eas-Coul-Aulin ("The Beautiful Fall of Coul"), near the far end of Loch Glencoul in Sutherland, is one of the finest of all Scottish waterfalls. The Amhainn an Loch Bhig burn, which has its source in a series of desolate mountain tarns, plunges over the precipitous slopes of Leitir Dubh (from a height three times that of Niagara) about a mile from the head of Loch Beag, and forms the Eas-Coul-Aulin. Owing to the general contour of the land, the only feasible way of reaching it is by boat from Kylescu Ferry.

From Loch Glencoul, the first glimpse of the upper portion of this fall is fully three miles distant, hurling itself over a perpendicular cliff, embedded in a perfect den of nature. Silhouetted against the grim rocks, this foaming mountain torrent is savage in the extreme, as its waters with one wild leap plunge over the dizzy brink to be churned into spray in the steaming depths below. Near its base the fall splits into a number of cascades spreading out in fan formation, where it encounters a jutting ledge of rock.

There is a legend attached to this fall concerning a beautiful maiden, the personification of perfect womanhood, with blue eyes and "golden tresses like a real princess," whose parents once tried to force her to marry a man whose amours she had rejected, having previously pledged herself to another. This suitor she loved with all her heart. Driven almost frantic by pressure to marry the wealthy young man of her parents' choice, she fled for refuge to the mountains. Finally, a search party was organised, headed by the young man she was being forced to wed.

This party followed her along the top of the Leitir Dubh, and just as the leader was in the act of clasping her in his arms, rather than yield to his clutches, she flung herself over the cataract, to be dashed to pieces on the rocks below, when the waters immediately took the shape of the girl's waving hair and flowing tresses.

According to the local story, on bright moonlight nights this mythical damsel can still be seen lying near the base of the fall, her wondrous eyes gazing heavenwards and a sweet smile on her lips, as the ever-sounding fall waves her golden locks in its waters.

Murdering pirates and Raven's gold

Beneath a small grassy plot near a rowan tree, upon an eminence on the rocky shore of Loch Cairnbawn, West Sutherland, there are said to rest, in an old wooden chest, the pickled heart and intestines of a Swedish prince. He is believed to have met his death in a mysterious way. According to an old local legend, this Swedish prince set sail to Scotland against his mother's wishes, with a cargo of gold. The reason he took with him so valuable a shipment is uncertain, but it is said that before he left Sweden his mother, who was gifted with second sight, had tried her utmost to dissuade him, and warned him that if he must embark upon the voyage, he should "steer clear of Cape Wrath and the dark Bay of Torogowan," as she foresaw a calamity. Despite her timely warning, the prince set out for the Scottish mainland.

When his vessel approached Cape Wrath there was dense fog which lasted several days and nights. The prince, remembering his mother's solemn warning, was much perplexed and a trifle alarmed. After a long time, a foreign vessel suddenly loomed up alongside out of the haze, and the Swede, not knowing his bearings, shouted out to the crew: "Where are we?"

"You are in Torogowan Bay," came the reply. Scarcely had the words been exchanged than the crew of the foreign vessel boarded the Swedish boat, and on discovering the treasure, murdered the prince and his crew and escaped with the gold. Not long after, the body of the prince was buried on a rocky promontory by the shore of Loch Cairnbawn. (His remains were afterwards exhumed, disembowelled, embalmed with salt and taken back for interment in his native land. His entrails, however (which were also preserved in salt) were placed inside a wooden chest and put back in the same grave by the side of the sea loch.)

On learning of the murder, the local people hurried to the scene of the atrocity and, after pronouncing a curse upon the pirates, gave chase. The robbers jettisoned most of their spoil into Loch Cairnbawn, but one of the pirates named Osckit — a man of titanic strength — continued overland with a sack of gold. The men of Sutherland followed closely but Osckit gave them a hard race, and when he reached the two big rocks of Dornie, sprang across them, leaving his pursuers behind. This feat had never been accomplished before. Osckit made good his escape, concealing the gold inside a certain cairn by the sea-shore.

Some time afterwards while Osckit and two of his confederates were poaching near the head of Badcall Bay, a strange vessel suddenly appeared in the estuary. A bullet from the ship pierced Osckit through the heart. He tried to explain to his accomplices where he had hidden the gold, but his speech was inarticulate as his strength was far spent, and before he expired all he was able to mutter was: "It is I who deserved it. It is I who got it."

Immediately the ship faded from sight a witch appeared to the two remaining brigands and said to them: "Tha an t-or anns a' charn. ("The gold is in the cairn"). Just before the witch disappeared, a raven was seen to perch on her shoulder, and she vowed that the shade of Osckit would haunt the shores of Loch Cairnbawn each night until all the stolen treasure should be found, but that the finder would meet an untimely and violent death. Some time afterwards, so runs the legend, a local crofter who had heard of these strange happenings dreamt about the hidden gold, and so vivid was his dream, that he walked to the place which he had seen in his vision the previous night, and had no difficulty in locating the cairn. He arrived at the burial place as the sun was setting, but on observing a huge raven perched above it, he fled in terror from the spot muttering to himself: "Dubh mar a chiste laidhe!" ("Black as a coffin!"). He died shortly afterwards without divulging the site of the cairn to anyone.

Within recent years, it is said, another smallholder of the district happened to be walking along the rocky shore of Loch Cairnbawn one moonlight night when suddenly a raven swooped over his head and he stumbled over something while crossing a mound of stones between some boulders, and his foot sank into a sandy hollow. On withdrawing his leg, he felt what he assumed to be some grit enter his boot; but believing that some small pebbles had found their way inside it, he did not bother to remove his boot, because he had not far to walk to his dinghy in order to row home. When eventually he did reach his croft, to his astonishment he discovered that what he had supposed to be pebbles were two gold coins.

Recalling a saying which he had learned when a youth, that the cairn in which the gold was hidden would be distinguished by the presence of a raven perched on top of it, he thought that discretion would be the better part of valour, and returned the next evening to the same spot, and replaced the coins in the sand. None the less he was drowned that same night while attempting to row home in the teeth of a violent storm.

Some thirty-five few years ago, two Edinburgh gentlemen spending a holiday at Kylescu Ferry Inn, being interested in the story of the Swedish prince, visited the supposed site of the prince's grave. On digging down, they came upon an old wooden box. In it were what appeared to be the shrivelled remains of human entrails; but being somewhat taken aback at the sudden appearance of a raven, and no doubt a trifle scared, they forthwith replaced the lid and buried the receptacle again, lest some misfortune might befall them.

According to another old story, the place where the gold is said to be concealed can only be found by following a raven which will be seen perched on top of one of three different cairns in the neighbourhood, and that: "Nuair bhios a ghealach lan seallaidh am fitheach an carn anns a bheil an t-or am falach" ("When the moon is full, the raven will point out the cairn inside which the gold is hidden"), by flitting from one cairn to another until it finally rests on the actual cairn. To this day, nobody knows the exact spot.

The Haunted Bridge

The Drochaid-Mhor ("Big Bridge") spans the River Dionard, near Durness, a stretch of water that was at one time the best for salmon. The Dionard flows out of Loch Dionard, in Strath Dionard, one of the dreariest and wildest-looking straths in Sutherland.

In the days when the Drochaid-Mhor was built the science of bridge building in the Highlands must have been little known; or, perhaps the people of the Highlands had a style of their own, as all the bridges had a centre like the back of a dromedary. No matter how deep the chasm to be bridged over — the back of the bridge had to be several feet above the level of the road. A most ridiculous and curious-looking affair it was, and very trying to horses coming from a level road to have to climb so suddenly. Drochaid-Mhor is a very good example of this style.

It was, and still is, haunted by many goblins — said to make themselves visible to chosen mortals. But sometimes these immortal beings go too far, as in the case of a certain mail gig driver, who left Rhiconich late one wintry, stormy night for Durness, with mail bags but no passengers. He could not have been blamed for worshipping at the shrine of Bacchus before he left the inn, seeing that he had twelve miles of dreary road to traverse, and the Drochaid-Mhor to cross, at which place he frequently encountered the nightly spectres. Indeed, he was beginning to form an intimate acquaintance with them, because often the kindly ones accompanied him some distance beyond the bridge. But this night was particularly bleak and tempestuous, the wind and snow coming down Strath Dionard with a force that almost overturned horse and machine on the road.

The next morning the good people of Durness were anxious because the mail had not arrived, and several of the men volunteered to go in search of the driver. As they wandered along the road to within a mile of Drochaid-Mhor a black object was seen in the distance, making hard to meet them. Some proposed to go off the road until the object passed, others of more courage offered to face it. On its approach it was found to be the horse, but no man or machine was to be seen. The horse seemed very frightened, and was with some difficulty taken back along the road.

Near to the end of the bridge was found the machine upset on the roadside and, still nearer the bridge, the driver, in a semi-conscious state. With considerable difficulty he was able to communicate to his rescuers that the goblins had attacked him while he was crossing the bridge. He was carried home, but never regained consciousness, and died a few days later. For many a day after it was with no small trouble that a man could be induced to drive the mails at night, unless accompanied by two or three others. However, as time wore on, the long summer days arrived, and the phantoms kept within reasonable bounds, a man was persuaded once more to drive the mails alone.

All the various tales of bridge goblin hauntings related in print would make a book of some size — from their eldrich and unearthly sounds and groans, the innumerable blinks of lights, the noiseless and peculiar-looking horses, not to mention the ghosts of several men and women drowned in different parts of the river. All these seemed to collect here, and appear to the lonely night wayfarer. An honest drainer once told me that he had the company of a woman who was dressed in black, along the road to the bridge one night. She appeared anxious to have a chat with him, but he declined to say a single word, and after a long look at him she vanished out of sight.

A man of some importance, and a regular attendant at religious meetings, told me also that he witnessed a strange vision at this bridge, as he was one night returning from visiting a friend at Carraigbhreac. When within 200 yards of the bridge, he observed a curious being, tall and slender, rising from the riverside, dressed in pure white and making direct for him. He at once made off, and was able to cross the centre of the bridge before the spectre came up to him. The hideous squeal it gave after him when it found itself unable to cross the key-stone of the bridge was reminiscent of Cutty Sark of Alloway.

A conclusion reached by some of the local people is that the bridge is to fall under a crowded coach or similar conveyance, and that the passengers will perish in the river. This is the reason for the lights, the ghosts and the phantom coaches.

A Famous Highland Poacher

"A fish from the pool and a deer from the mountain are thefts no man need be ashamed of." — *Gaelic saying.*

The Highland poacher of old was never regarded as a criminal in the strict sense of the word, and he himself never considered he was doing anything wrong. Even although poaching was sometimes his sole activity, he regarded it as a hobby. He also kept to a strict moral code all his own, and never resorted to the use of poison or explosives. He poached because he enjoyed it as a sport. He never boasted, but was at the height of emotional fulfilment while carrying home his spoil.

An old man told me that about a century ago Navidale, a hamlet a mile from Helmsdale, was noted for the poaching activites of the villagers. "There was," said the old man, "a noted poacher called Donald, who went in for deer. In the late harvest, and always accompanied by his son, he would get up about three or four o'clock in the morning, and yoke the horse with the ostensible purpose of going for a load of peats. If, however, you looked into the straw at the bottom of the cart, you would find a sporting rifle and other implements not necessary for carrying peats at all."

Having arrived at the moss, Donald would shoulder his rifle, leave the horse with his son, and proceed to the spot where he knew the deer came to drink. Having concealed himself, he would select the one which suited his purpose best. Sometimes a good deal of stalking was necessary, but the result was always the same — Donald killed his deer. When the son heard the report of the rifle, he would hurry to the spot, knowing that he was required to help move a stag.

With a few skilled rips of his long knife, the entrails were removed and buried. The carcase was carried to the cart and covered with straw, and peats put on in the usual way. Donald and his son then returned to Navidale with their first "load of peats" shortly after daybreak. Having emptied the peats at the peat stack, the cart was quickly brought to the barn-door close by, the deer hauled inside, skinned and cut into convenient pieces, which were often distributed among friends in Helmsdale.

"Another poacher," continued the old man, "whom I will call Sandy, was well known in Sutherland and Caithness. He knew all the corries, glens and hills in both counties, and fully believed that 'wild beasts' were intended for the use of man.

"A south country gentleman introduced to Sandy by a friend, promised to pay a large sum if he got a stag to his own gun. He would, he said, pay all expenses, and take the risks involved in forays among deer on any of the hills in Sutherland and Caithness. So it came about that the gentleman, his servant and a Highland pony met Sandy and his friend at a corrie half-way between Auchintoul and Forsinard. After judicious stalking they came to a herd of deer, from which the gentleman culled one good stag, and Sandy another.

"The party had just taken an early breakfast and were preparing to clear off with their booty, when two of the shooting tenants came upon them and claimed the deer as their property. One of them was rather assertive, and so was tumbled into the burn. The other then interfered, whereupon the gentleman called upon his servant to put a double charge in his gun and 'shoot the blackguards.' This so frightened the men that they hastened back to Auchintoul for assistance.

"On returning they found the poaching party had decamped, taking the deer with them, and were nearly out of sight over the hills towards Caithness. Sandy remained behind and got involved in a scuffle with the landlord of the inn, so that his party might have time to get clear away. The innkeeper tried to take the gun from Sandy, but Sandy got the better of him and took *his* gun and threw it into a nearby quagmire. Sandy then took to his heels and escaped.

"The English gentleman got both heads, and paid Sandy well. He also sent Sandy a fine new rifle and many complimentary letters, in one of which he said he would give a hundred pounds for 'another year's fun'."

"The Red Hanging Judge"

Many years ago a supreme magistrate named *Am Breve Ruadh* of the Hebrides, earned the local title of "The Red Hanging Judge" on account of the ruthless and vindictive sentences which he frequently imposed. The penalties he passed were so cruel that he was ultimately compelled to flee from the Lewis to shelter in North West Scotland. There he lived in seclusion for some time with an old woman in a lonely croft on the hillside overlooking Inverkirkaig Bay; but his whereabouts were ultimately discovered by a Lewisman named Asgaig who tracked him to the banks of a remote loch in Ross-shire where he stabbed the Judge to death. On account of this incident, the

The Red Hanging Judge.

loch inherited the name of *Loch Sgian Asgaig* (modern spelling Sionsgaig) — "The Loch of Asgaig's Knife."

The murderer trailed the Judge's body some miles distant over rough country and dug a grave near a croft at Inverkirkaig (on the coast road between Lochinver and Ullapool), marked by a long flat slab of reddish stone to this day.

Some time after the murder, Asgaig's dead body was found in a loch to the north-west of Badygyle by the road to Achiltbibuie. This loch was named Loch Osgaig after him by his friends, and still retains the name.

Less than half a century ago, a Canadian relative of the present tenant of the croft, while on holiday at Inverkirkaig, raised the slab of stone one autumn afternoon and found underneath a number of beautiful pebbles. He collected a few of them and placed them on his bedroom mantelpiece in an upper room of the cottage.

That very same night a violent thunderstorm occurred, waking all the inhabitants of the neighbourhood. One peal of thunder alone is said to have reverberated amid the hills for over an hour and to this day, the event is referred to locally as "The night of the Storm." The croft shook and vibrated, the beds swayed to and fro, and the doors and windows rattled.

Suddenly, at the height of the storm, the crofter's brother and his wife, as they sat up in bed, beheld a bluish-green light on the mantelshelf where the pebbles lay. In a frenzy of bewilderment and fear, the crofter's brother leapt out of bed and seizing hold of his trophies threw them seaward out of the window. No sooner had he done so than the storm subsided, and a great calm reigned.

In the morning a search was made for the pebbles, but not a single one could be found.

According to local tradition, the Judge resented the interference with his grave and his earthly belongings.

Can it be that they are once again beneath the slab marking the lonely grave of Inverkirkaig?